CHRISTMAS REVISITED

© 2007 by Faber Music Ltd
First published by Faber Music Ltd in 2007
3 Queen Square, London WC1N 3AU

Arranged by Olly Weeks
Edited by Lucy Holliday

Designed by Lydia Merrills-Ashcroft

Printed in England by Caligraving Ltd

The text paper used in this publication is a virgin fibre product that is manufactured in the UK
to ISO 14001 standards. The wood fibre used is only sourced from managed forests using
sustainable forestry principles. This paper is 100% recyclable

ISBN10: 0-571-53099-0
EAN13: 978-0-571-53099-1

To buy Faber Music publications or to find out about the full range of titles available,
please contact your local music retailer or Faber Music sales enquiries:

Faber Music Ltd, Burnt Mill, Elizabeth Way, Harlow, CM20 2HX England
Tel: +44(0)1279 82 89 82 Fax: +44(0)1279 82 89 83
sales@fabermusic.com fabermusic.com

THE CHRISTMAS SONG
(CHESTNUTS ROASTING ON AN OPEN FIRE)

Words and Music by Mel Tormé and Robert Wells

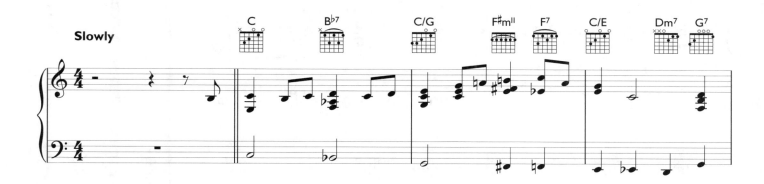

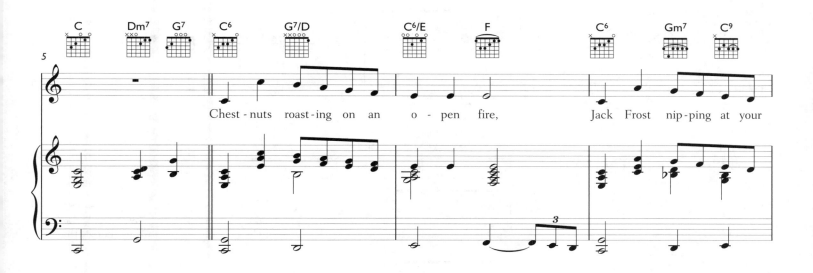

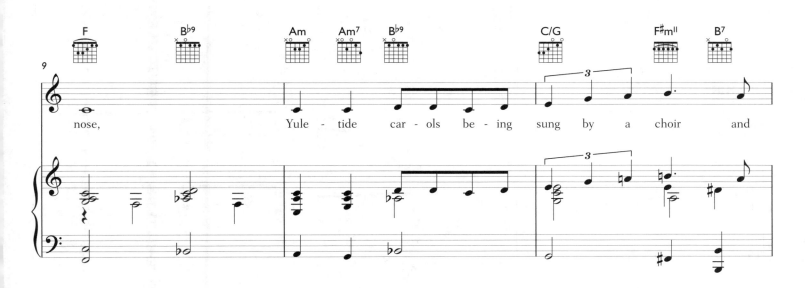

CHRISTMAS TIME ALL OVER THE WORLD

Words and Music by Hugh Martin

CHRISTMAS TIME IS HERE

Words and Music by Vince Guaraldi and Lee Mendelson

Sleigh-bells in the air, beau-ty ev-'ry-where,

Yule-tide by the fi-re-side and joy-ful mem-'ries there.

Christ-mas-time is here, fam-'lies grow-ing near,

HAVE YOURSELF A MERRY LITTLE CHRISTMAS

Words and Music by Hugh Martin and Ralph Blane

Through the years we all will be tog-eth-er if the fates_ al - low,

I BELIEVE

Words by Sammy Cahn
Music by Jule Styne

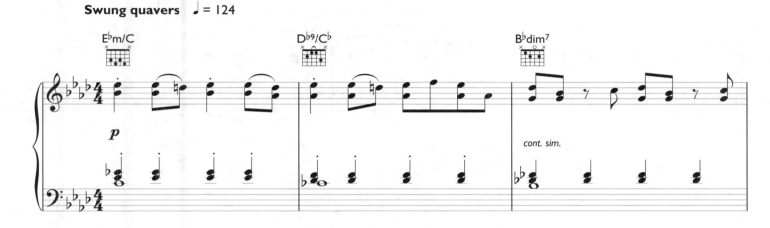

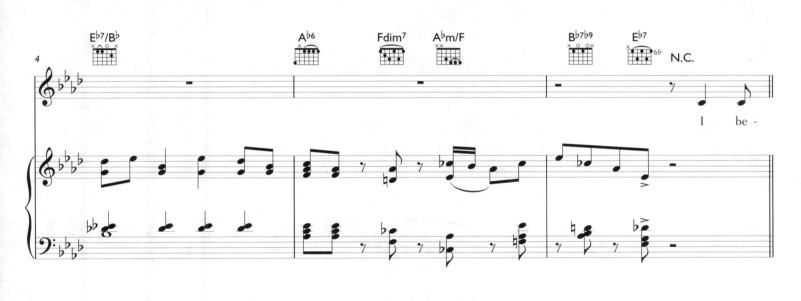

na - ive, but that's what, that's what I be - lieve.____

I HEARD THE BELLS ON CHRISTMAS DAY

Words by Henry Longfellow
Music by Johnny Marks

1. I heard the bells on Christmas Day, their old familiar carols play,
2. I thought how as the day had come the belfries of all Christendom

and wild and sweet the words repeat
had rung so long the unbroken song

of peace on Earth, goodwill to men.

I'LL BE HOME FOR CHRISTMAS

Words and Music by Kim Gannon, Walter Kent and Buck Ram

I'VE GOT MY LOVE TO KEEP ME WARM

Words and Music by Irving Berlin

LET IT SNOW! LET IT SNOW! LET IT SNOW!

Words by Sammy Cahn
Music by Jule Styne

O COME O COME EMMANUEL

Traditional
Arranged by Sufjan Stevens

PEACE

Words and Music by Horace Silver

the free-dom you seek is one. Peace is for ev - 'ry- one,

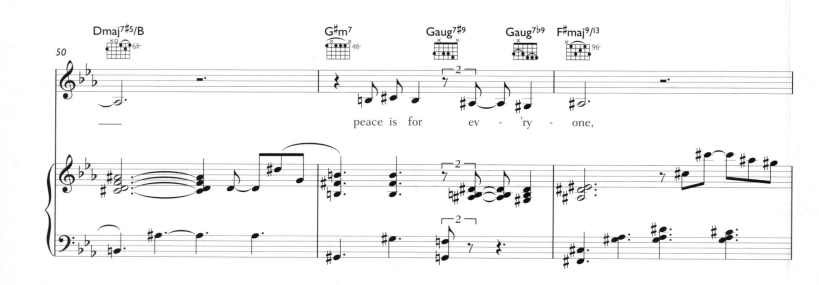

peace is for ev - 'ry - one,

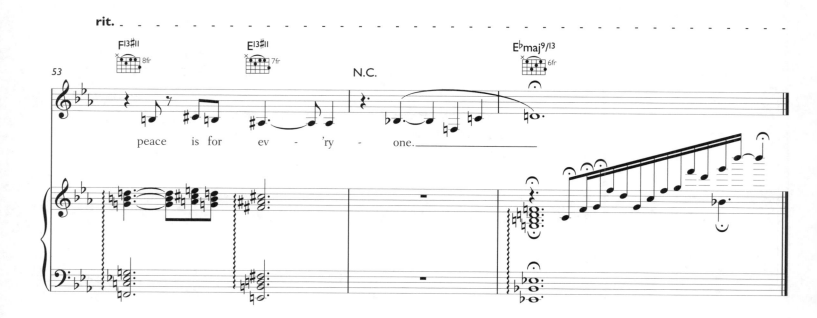

rit.

peace is for ev - 'ry - one.

RUDOLPH THE RED NOSED REINDEER

Words and Music by Johnny Marks

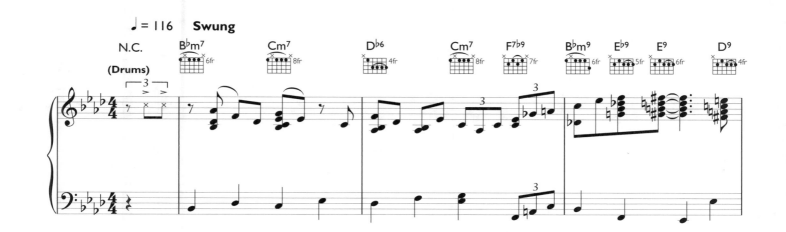

Hang your nose down Ru - dy, _____

SANTA CLAUS IS COMING TO TOWN

Words by Haven Gillespie
Music by Fred J Coots

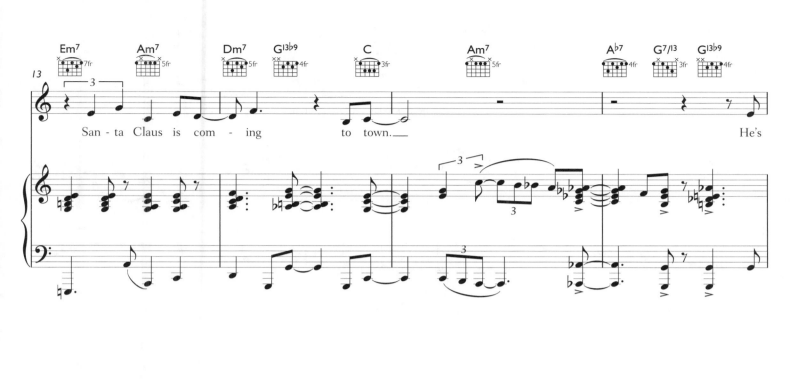

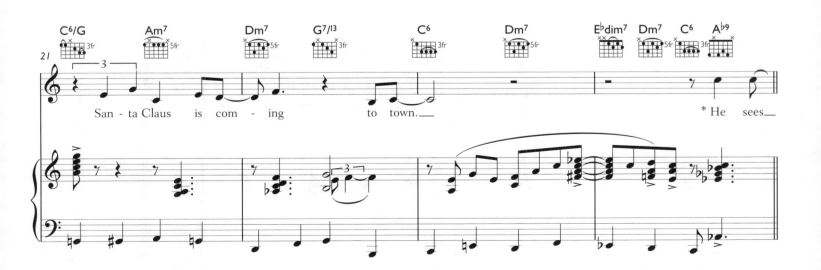

SLEIGH RIDE

Words by Mitchell Parish
Music by Leroy Anderson

love - ly weath - er for a sleigh ride tog - eth - er with you. Out - side the

snow is fal - ling and friends are cal - ling:"Yoo - hoo!" Come on, it's

love - ly weath - er for a sleigh ride tog - eth - er with you. Gid - dy

WHITE CHRISTMAS

Words and Music by Irving Berlin

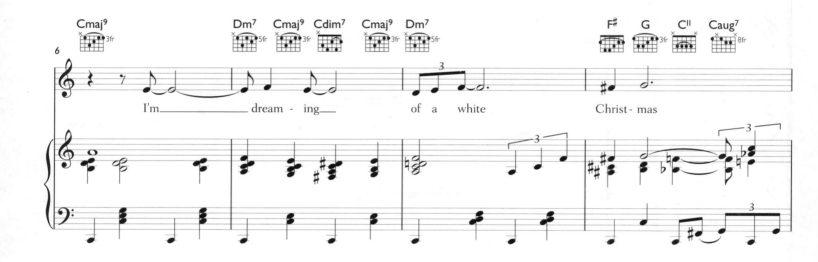

WINTER WONDERLAND

Words by Dick Smith
Music by Felix Bernard

WHAT ARE YOU DOING NEW YEARS EVE?

Words and Music by Frank Loesser

Free tempo, ad lib. swung quavers throughout